Dungeon Danger

Steve Barlow and Steve Skidmore ◼ Jonatronix

Buckminster Primary School
School Lane
Buckminster
Grantham
NG33 5RZ
Tel: 01476 860315

OXFORD
UNIVERSITY PRESS

Tiger and his friends are enjoying a day at the castle. Re-enactors are showing visitors how people lived in the past.

The children dress as knights in armour and enter a competition to make model siege engines.

Dr X's henchmen, Plug and Socket, disguise themselves and trap Cat and Tiger.

Cat and Tiger use their siege engines to escape. Dr X has another plan. The children must be on their guard …

Chapter 1 – A lucky break

The Red Knight knocked his opponent's sword out of his hand. The Blue Knight fell to his knees and opened his visor. "I yield!" he cried.

Max, Cat, Ant and Tiger clapped loudly as the tournament ended.

"That was excellent," said Tiger. "Can we explore more of the castle now?"

Max looked around. "All right – but keep an eye out for Dr X's henchmen. Remember they are disguised as a minstrel and a jester."

"Then we should be able to spot them a mile off," said Ant.

Cat spotted a sign. "Hey – look at this!"

Dungeon

Meet the Knights of the Round Table!

Visit the dungeon and see
King Arthur prepare
for his last battle!
Exciting special effects
Buy your tickets at the gatehouse
(Exhibit closes at 5pm)

"I'd like to see the dungeon," said Cat.

Ant frowned. "Is the dungeon a good place to be if Dr X's henchmen are around?"

"It won't be a dark, dirty prison like it was in the past," Max pointed out. "It should be as safe as anywhere else in the castle."

Tiger beamed. "Let's go! If it's about a battle, there's bound to be more fighting."

"We'll need to get some tickets though," said Cat.

Just then, two re-enactors appeared. They were wearing chain mail armour with surcoats. The visors were down on their helmets.

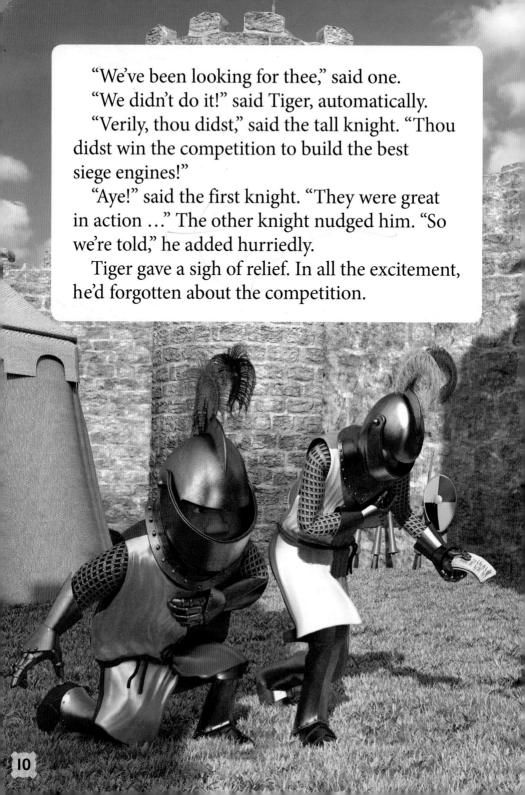

"We've been looking for thee," said one.

"We didn't do it!" said Tiger, automatically.

"Verily, thou didst," said the tall knight. "Thou didst win the competition to build the best siege engines!"

"Aye!" said the first knight. "They were great in action …" The other knight nudged him. "So we're told," he added hurriedly.

Tiger gave a sigh of relief. In all the excitement, he'd forgotten about the competition.

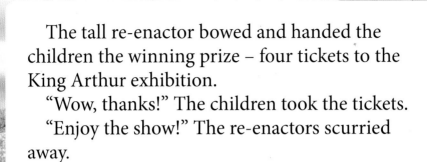

The tall re-enactor bowed and handed the children the winning prize – four tickets to the King Arthur exhibition.

"Wow, thanks!" The children took the tickets.

"Enjoy the show!" The re-enactors scurried away.

"That's lucky." Max waved his ticket in the air. "It looks as if we'll get to see the exhibition after all. Come on."

The children headed through the door to the dungeon. They didn't notice the re-enactors watching them from afar.

The shorter one raised the visor on his helmet. "They fell for it!"

"Come on, let's follow them," Socket said.

Chapter 2 – Into the depths

The children followed the signs to the dungeon down a stone staircase. The deeper they went, the darker it became.

"We must be deep under the castle by now." Tiger's voice echoed eerily around the stone walls.

They came to a corridor that was lit by flickering electric lights made to look like flaming torches. There were lots of tiny rooms either side of the corridor. Max looked in one. "I bet these were cells for prisoners," he said.

Ant shivered.

Dungeon this way ⟶

Just outside the door to the dungeon, Tiger pointed. "Hey, what are those?"

"Stocks," said Cat. "They were a punishment. If you'd done something bad, you'd have to sit in them while people threw rotten eggs and cabbages at you."

Tiger was puzzled. "How do you mean, sit in them?"

Cat and Ant opened the stocks and Max pointed. "You'd put your ankles in those holes. When the stocks were closed, you couldn't get your feet out. You'd be stuck there until the sheriff let you go."

"Like this?" Tiger sat with his ankles in the holes.

Cat grinned at Ant. "Shall we?" She started to close the stocks.

"No!" said Max quickly. "Tiger might get stuck."

Cat laughed. "It's a good job we don't have stocks at school, Tiger. You're in trouble so often, you'd never be out of them!"

"Oh, very funny. Ha ha!" Tiger pulled a face and headed for the dungeon door. "Come on! I want to see the show."

Meanwhile ...

Plug tripped on the last step and almost fell. "I can't see a thing!" he moaned.

"Put your visor up, then!" snapped Socket.

"Oh, yeah." Plug raised his visor and spotted the children at the far end of the corridor. He stifled a giggle. "They're going into the dungeon!"

"Sssh!" hissed Socket. The children disappeared through the door. "Wait until they see what Dr X has planned for them!"

Chapter 3 – The dungeon

The dungeon was very spooky. There were only a few dim torches on the walls. Shadows filled the rest of the room.

Several visitors were watching a group of fierce-looking knights in armour. The knights were wearing helmets with the visors raised. Their voices echoed round the room.

"My Lord," said one, raising a squeaky arm, "Sir Lancelot is a traitor!"

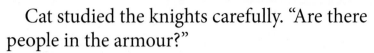

Cat studied the knights carefully. "Are there people in the armour?"

Ant shook his head. He explained that the suits of armour had machinery inside, controlled by a computer. That was how the knights were able to move. Actors had been filmed speaking the knights' lines and the film was being projected onto screens inside their helmets.

"Oh, I see," said Cat. "It's very lifelike."

"It's very boring!" said Tiger crossly. "They're just talking! Why don't they get on with the fighting?"

The lights in the dungeon brightened and the knights became still. The other visitors started to leave.

"Oh, it's finished!" Ant was disappointed. "We missed most of it."

"It was boring anyway," said Tiger.

Ant folded his arms. "Well, I want to wait and see the whole thing."

Max checked his watch. "All right. We've got time before the dungeon closes."

Max, Cat and Ant waited patiently for the scene to play again. Tiger scowled and scuffed his feet on the floor.

They didn't notice the two faces that peered at them through the door.

However, they did hear the door slam shut.

Cat was nearest the door. She ran to it and pushed hard. "We're locked in!"

Chapter 4 – NASTI knights

"Locked in?" said Max. "We can't be."

"Well, we are!" said Cat. "We're trapped."

Max checked his watch. "They shouldn't be closing the dungeon for another hour."

"What do we do now?" asked Cat.

"I'll call for help on my phone," said Max. He checked the screen and gave a grunt of dismay. "No good. There's no signal. We must be too far underground."

"Oh, great!" Tiger was fed up. "We wait down here for this boring show and then get locked in. Now these stupid knights aren't even doing anything!" He marched up to the nearest suit of armour and kicked it.

With a creaking noise, the armour turned its helmeted head towards Tiger. The alert signal on Tiger's watch began to flash. He stared at it in horror. "X-bots – that's all we need!"

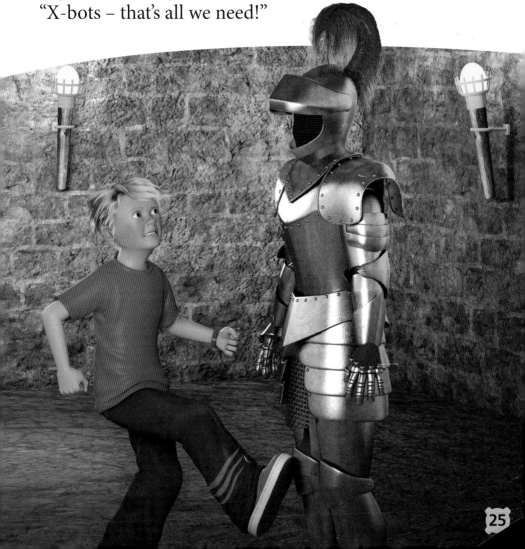

The suit of armour shot out a metal fist. The steel gauntlet closed round Tiger's arm in a vice-like grip. He struggled to get free but it was no use.

"Help!" he yelled. "It's got me!"

"What's happening?" wailed Cat. "Where are the X-bots?"

"I think they're inside the knights." Ant sounded scared.

Cat turned to Max. "The X-bots have taken control of the computers inside the armour!"

"Very clever, young man." An eerie voice echoed round the dungeon. The knight's screen flickered to reveal a familiar face.

"We meet at last – and my X-bots have you at my mercy!"

Chapter 5 – Dr X takes charge

"It's Dr X!" cried Cat.

"Now we're really in trouble," added Max.

Dr X raised his voice. "Come in, you fools!"

The door to the dungeon opened and the two re-enactors came in with their visors up.

Ant groaned. "Dr X's henchmen! They've changed their disguise."

"We should have known!" said Max. He turned a determined face to Ant and Cat. "Get ready to run."

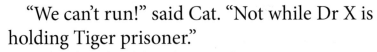

"We can't run!" said Cat. "Not while Dr X is holding Tiger prisoner."

Max clenched his fists in frustration.

"Quite right, young lady," said the gloating voice of Dr X. "Don't worry, no harm will come to you. I only want my watches back."

Socket waved his hand in the air. "Shall we take the watches off them, boss?"

Dr X glared. "No! You are so incompetent, you'll only lose them."

Plug sniffed. "That's not very nice."

"Well, he is the boss of NASTI," Socket reminded him.

"Get out of here and guard the door!" roared Dr X. "No matter what happens, you are NOT to open the door – and you are NOT to touch my precious watches!"

Muttering angrily, Plug and Socket did as they were told.

Dr X gave his captives an evil grin. "Soon I will have my watches back. Then my X-machine will be complete and I can take over the world – and there is nothing you can do to stop me!"

Chapter 6 – Rooted to the spot

Dr X's laughter filled the dungeon as the other three suits of armour came to life. Their joints squeaked and squealed as they turned towards Max, Cat and Ant.

"Get ready to dodge around them!" said Max.

The knights reached towards the children – but something was wrong. Only the upper parts of their armoured bodies were moving.

"What's happening?" Dr X cried. "Why aren't my knights moving?"

The armour groaned as the knights tried to walk. The knight holding Tiger tried a bit too hard. It overbalanced and went crashing to the ground. Tiger was free!

Ant smiled. "I know what's happened! The knights only have machinery in their arms, heads and bodies. They don't have any in their legs because they're not supposed to walk …"

Max grinned. "So there's nothing for the X-bots to control!"

"Blast!" snarled Dr X. He raised his voice. "Plug! Socket! I need you. Come and take the watches!"

"Oh, no!" The voices of Dr X's henchmen called faintly from outside the door.

"You told us NOT to open the door and NOT to touch the watches. This could be a trick!" Plug said.

"We're obeying orders, we are!" added Socket.

Tiger bounced in front of the helpless knights. "Can't catch me!"

"You can't escape!" snarled Dr X. "My X-bots will see to that!"

The screens in the suits of armour slid away. The knights stopped moving as the X-bots controlling them poured out and headed straight for the children.

"Time to go!" shouted Max.

The friends sprinted across the room. Max spotted a small crack in the bottom of the door. He gave the signal. The children turned the dials on their watches. They pushed the X and …

They squeezed through the crack just in time. Tiger peered back to see the X-bots' red eyes glinting back furiously. Their heads were too large to fit through.

Chapter 7 – Stuck in the stocks

Plug and Socket were standing with their backs to the door.

"There's a lot of shouting coming from in there," said Socket.

"Fancy those kids trying to fool us," chuckled Plug.

"They really did sound like the boss, didn't they?" laughed Socket.

"Oh, look." Plug pointed at the stocks. "There's a bench just there. All this standing around is hurting my feet. I think I'll sit down for a moment."

"Me, too," said Socket. "Look, there are places to put your ankles so you can stretch out properly."

Plug gave a contented sigh. "How thoughtful."

They were so busy relaxing, they didn't see the children creeping up on them.

A moment later, Max, Cat, Ant and Tiger pressed the buttons on their watches. They grew back to normal size.

Plug blinked. "How did you lot escape?"

Ant didn't say anything. He'd noticed that Plug and Socket were sitting with their ankles in the stocks. He grinned at Tiger. Tiger winked back.

A moment later, the boys had dropped the top half of the stocks and locked it in place. It was the henchmen's turn to be trapped!

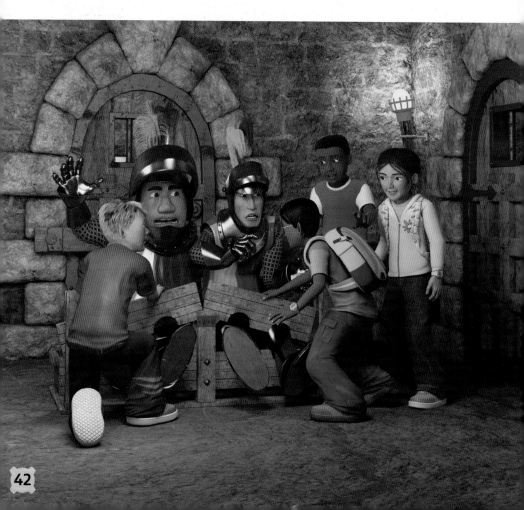

"Here!" said Plug. "I can't move my feet …"

"Serves you right!" said Cat. She gave Dr X's hapless henchmen a wave as she followed Max, Ant and Tiger up the stairs to safety. "Bye!"

Plug gave Socket a sheepish look. "That could have gone better …"

Socket shook his head gloomily. "I don't think the boss is going to be very pleased with us …"

Chapter 8 – Another fine mess …

The children raced to the top of the stairs and out into the fresh air. Cat slammed the door shut.

"I wouldn't want to be Dr X's henchmen right now," chuckled Ant.

Tiger grinned. "What a knight-mare!" he said.

Back at NASTI HQ, Dr X was not in a good mood. He was so purple with rage, his face almost matched his suit.

"You fools!" he bawled at Plug and Socket. "You let my watches slip from your grasp – again!"

"But you said we weren't to touch the watches!" Plug replied.

Dr X wasn't listening. "My brilliant plan! Ruined!"

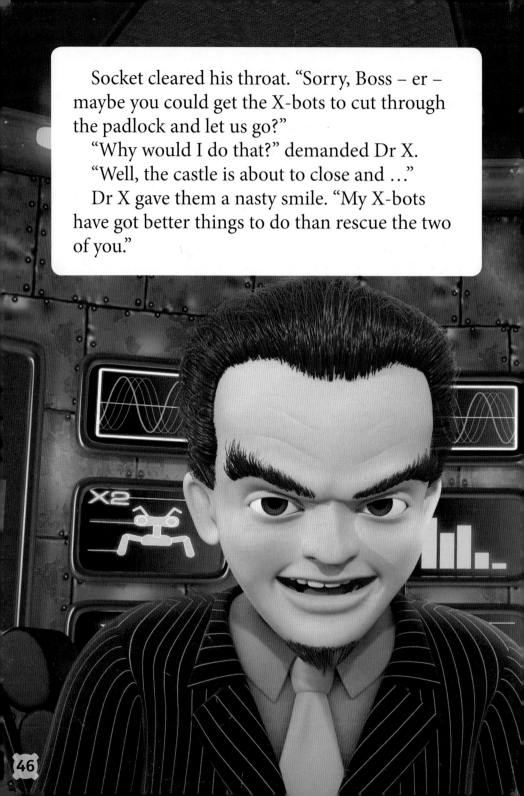

Socket cleared his throat. "Sorry, Boss – er – maybe you could get the X-bots to cut through the padlock and let us go?"

"Why would I do that?" demanded Dr X.

"Well, the castle is about to close and …"

Dr X gave them a nasty smile. "My X-bots have got better things to do than rescue the two of you."

Back in the castle, the lights started to go out, one by one.

"Oooooh!" moaned Plug.

"What's the matter?" demanded Socket.

"I'm scared of the dark," whimpered Plug.

Socket wriggled on the bench. His bottom had gone numb. "I'm starting to think," he said unhappily, "that working for an evil mastermind isn't all it's cracked up to be."

Find out what it takes to be a knight in *The Knight's Handbook.*

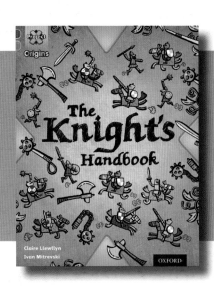

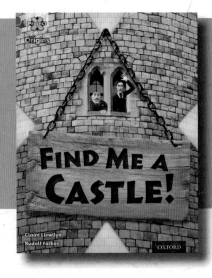

Discover more about different castles in *Find Me a Castle!*